THE
CAN'T SLEEP
COLOURING
JOURNAL

THE CAN'T SLEEP COLOURING JOURNAL

Dr Sarah Jane Arnold,
CPsychol

Michael O'Mara Books Limited

First published in Great Britain in 2016 by
Michael O'Mara Books Limited
9 Lion Yard
Tremadoc Road
London SW4 7NQ

A CIP catalogue record for this book is available from the British Library.

Papers used by Michael O'Mara Books Limited are natural, recyclable products
made from wood grown in sustainable forests. The manufacturing processes
conform to the environmental regulations of the country of origin.

ISBN: 978-1-78243-624-9 in paperback print format

1 2 3 4 5 6 7 8 9 10

www.mombooks.com

Cover design and illustration by Claire Cater
Designed by Ana Bjezancevic
Typeset by Jade Wheaton
Illustrations by Elzbieta Jarzabek, Victoria Nelson and Lizzie Preston

Every reasonable effort has been made to acknowledge all copyright holders.
Any errors or omissions that may have occurred are inadvertent, and anyone
with any copyright queries is invited to write to the publisher, so that full
acknowledgement may be included in subsequent editions of the work

Printed and bound in China

INTRODUCTION

Sleep is a universal, shared experience. It's something we all do, and it's something that we all need. Sometimes, sleep 'just happens' and we don't put much thought into it. Other times, sleeplessness can take centre stage in our awareness and we simply don't sleep how we want or need to. If you are currently experiencing poor sleep, *The Can't Sleep Colouring Journal* is here for you. Within this book, you will find beautiful designs to colour, accessible information about sleep and sleep problems, as well as helpful ways of responding to sleeplessness. We cannot force good-quality sleep, but we can learn how to enable it – and ourselves.

HOW WE SLEEP

Sleeping is a natural state of periodic rest that is regulated by the brain and influenced by our external environment. Each of us has an internal 'body clock', located within the brain, which works in accordance with the earth's 24-hour cycle of day and night. It regulates daily neurological and biological activities, and influences when we sleep and when we wake up (known as our circadian rhythms). During the daytime, our drive to sleep builds. The longer we stay awake, the greater the need for sleep becomes. When we fall asleep, the pressure to sleep is released – like a valve being opened – and the cycle begins again (a process called sleep-wake homeostasis).

Different people need and like different amounts of sleep, and how much sleep you require will depend upon factors such as your age and lifestyle. However, research suggests that around seven to eight hours of good-quality sleep per night is optimal for adults. Good-quality, restorative sleep positively affects our physical and mental health. It

supports the body to recharge and rejuvenate itself, allows the mind to have some respite from consciousness, and it helps us to process new information and consolidate memories.

SLEEP PROBLEMS

Many of us will experience poor sleep at some time during our lives. This may include finding it hard to fall asleep, difficulty staying asleep, poor-quality sleep (when you wake up feeling tired and don't feel rejuvenated), and/or waking up too early in the morning. Poor sleep can be caused by a multitude of different factors, including environmental factors, physical health problems, stressful life situations and emotional difficulties. It's common – and understandable – to fall into the trap of struggling with the experience of sleeplessness, but this tends to make the problem worse. It can create or worsen feelings of anxiety, stress, depression and helplessness associated with not sleeping as you want to.

RESPONDING TO SLEEPLESSNESS

We can't control sleeplessness, but we can choose how we respond to it. *The Can't Sleep Colouring Journal* provides an alternative, creative way of responding to poor sleep that puts your well-being first. It offers:

- Intricate designs to colour before bed or in response to sleeplessness, which may help you to feel relaxed and more ready for sleep when the time comes

- Inspirational quotes

- Helpful mantras to aid positive coping with sleeplessness

- Space to express and explore your thoughts and feelings

- Ways of tackling unhelpful thoughts that may be interfering with sleep

- Tips on how to establish a good sleep routine

- Encouragement to think about your lifestyle and ways of nurturing yourself when you can't sleep

The contents of this book are inspired by – and grounded in – Acceptance and Commitment Therapy (ACT) and Cognitive-Behavioural Therapy (CBT), which are proven to be helpful for people with sleep problems. Additionally, colouring can help to relax the mind in preparation for sleep and offers a helpful and enjoyable way of responding to poor sleep. So take this time for yourself, to reflect, express your thoughts and feelings, practise self-care and find joy in the present moment – even when you can't sleep.

With warm wishes,
Dr Sarah Jane Arnold

PUTTING TODAY TO BED

Take some time for yourself now
to reflect upon your day.

What went well?

What was challenging?

What, if anything, would you like
to do differently next time?

Doing this at the end of each day can help you to process and
make sense of your experiences so that your mind can rest.

'Sleeping is no mean art:
for its sake one must
stay awake all day.'

FRIEDRICH NIETZSCHE

EXPRESS YOURSELF

Writing in a journal offers you the opportunity to
think about who you are and what matters to you.
It also enables you to reflect upon anything that you
may be finding difficult or troubling at the moment.
These may be things that keep you up at night. Take
this opportunity now to express and explore what's
on your mind, and get to know yourself better.

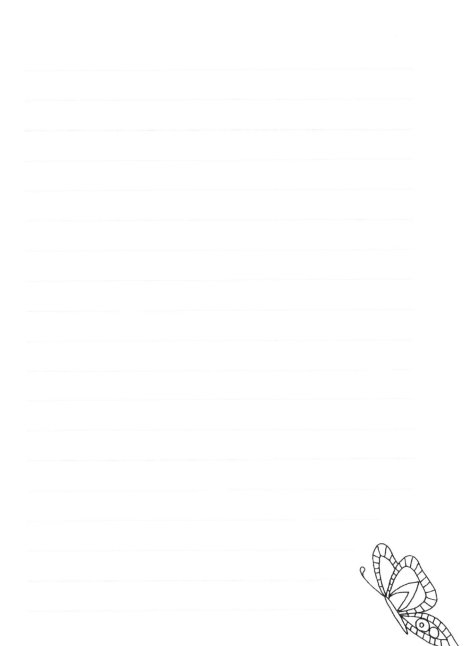

It's late, and I don't feel
ready to sleep yet.
I can accept this experience
without needing to like it.

I THINK THEREFORE I FEEL

When we have trouble sleeping, our minds
naturally think about the experience, have opinions
about it and try to make sense of it. Sometimes,
these thoughts can be unhelpful. If we buy into
them, they can cause us to feel challenging emotions
like stress and anxiety. Here are some examples
of the kinds of thoughts that people can have:

If I have less than eight hours' sleep, then I can't function.

This will ruin my day tomorrow.

I should go to bed earlier and try harder to sleep.

Perhaps you've had similar thoughts? Take a
moment to notice and write down any fears or
expectations that you have about not sleeping well,
and consider how these thoughts make you feel.

Now, see if you can reflect upon your thoughts.
Is this thought 100% true? Is it helpful? Is there
another, more helpful way of looking at this situation?
What advice would you give to a friend?

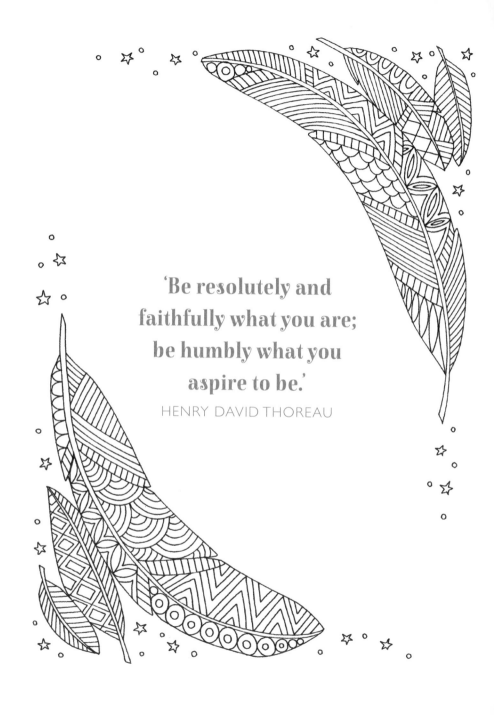

'Be resolutely and
faithfully what you are;
be humbly what you
aspire to be.'

HENRY DAVID THOREAU

A MOMENT OF APPRECIATION

When we have trouble sleeping, our minds can
create anxious thoughts about the experience and
what tomorrow will be like as a consequence of it.
The next time you notice these kinds of thoughts,
remind yourself that your mind is just doing its job.
Using its survival instinct, it's trying to keep you
safe from potential threats to your well-being.

Noticing what your mind is trying to do, and truly
appreciating it, helps your brain to feel heard and
understand that you are safe. This can help you
to feel less anxious. You can then respond to any
difficult thoughts (associated with sleeplessness)
from a more balanced, less reactive headspace.

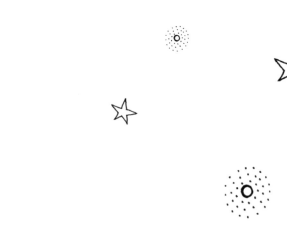

I will go to bed
when I feel sleepy.

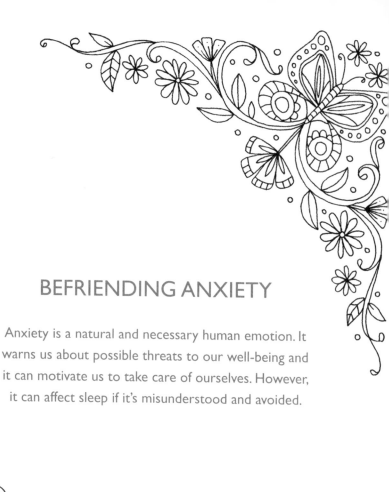

BEFRIENDING ANXIETY

Anxiety is a natural and necessary human emotion. It warns us about possible threats to our well-being and it can motivate us to take care of ourselves. However, it can affect sleep if it's misunderstood and avoided.

The next time you recognize the feeling of anxiety, see
if you can accept it and let it be with you. Explore it!
What are you feeling anxious or worried about? Try
to be as realistic as possible, and write about it here.

Say this does happen, how could you cope with it?
What would be helpful for you or the situation? Notice
what happens to your anxiety when you befriend it and
decide how you'll cope with the situation it's related to.

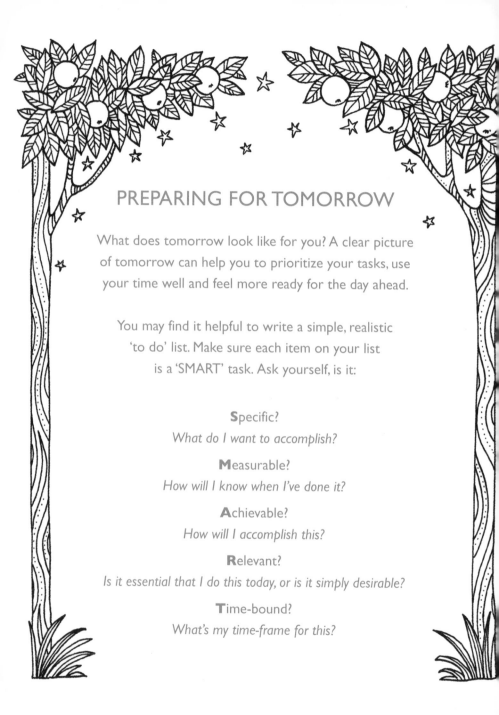

PREPARING FOR TOMORROW

What does tomorrow look like for you? A clear picture
of tomorrow can help you to prioritize your tasks, use
your time well and feel more ready for the day ahead.

You may find it helpful to write a simple, realistic
'to do' list. Make sure each item on your list
is a 'SMART' task. Ask yourself, is it:

Specific?
What do I want to accomplish?

Measurable?
How will I know when I've done it?

Achievable?
How will I accomplish this?

Relevant?
Is it essential that I do this today, or is it simply desirable?

Time-bound?
What's my time-frame for this?

When we have a realistic idea of the things that we'll do and a sense of how we'll cope with them, we're less prone to worry and stress. This can help us to feel more relaxed and sleep better.

'The greatest weapon against stress is our ability to choose one thought over another.'

WILLIAM JAMES

I can use
this time for me,
to connect with myself
and simply be.

PROBLEM-SOLVING

Problem-solving is a helpful way of dealing
with practical concerns that are affecting you
now and may be on your mind at night.

Step one: Clearly identify the problem
that you feel worried about.

Step two: Brainstorm and write down all
possible solutions to the problem, and consider
the pros and cons of each option.

Step three: Pick a solution and then outline the steps that you will take to solve the problem.

Step four: Check that each step in your plan is realistic and achievable, and begin tomorrow. Offer yourself some genuine praise for addressing this! Now you have a plan to deal with the situation.

'I loafe and invite
my soul, I lean and loafe
at my ease ... observing a
spear of summer grass.'

WALT WHITMAN

WHAT MAKES YOU HAPPY?

Living a rich and meaningful life can encourage good-quality sleep, so take a little time and consider this now. What makes *you* happy? What kinds of things would you like to do more of, or start doing? What matters to you?

Make a pact with yourself to plan and do some of these things,
no matter how simple or small they may seem. Decide upon one
thing that makes you smile, and do it for yourself tomorrow!

I will comfort and care
for myself now.

WHAT'S INSIDE

What we consume affects our sleep:

Caffeine (in energy drinks, coffee, teas, chocolate, etc.) and nicotine are stimulants that can interfere with the body's natural ability to fall asleep.

Foods that are high in sugar and those that are difficult to digest can disturb sleep. Eating a big meal before bed is also not recommended.

Alcohol can negatively affect the quality of your sleep, particularly if it's consumed in excess before you go to bed.

Try to avoid these for at least four hours before you go to bed, and monitor how you sleep over the course of a few weeks. What else might you enjoy? Time with loved-ones, a massage, meditation and colouring are all great alternatives to help your mind and body relax.

EXERCISE

Being physically active during the day can be very
beneficial for your mental and physical health,
and research tells us that exercise can help to
promote good-quality sleep. However, if you are
experiencing sleep problems, you may find it helpful
not to exercise after 6 p.m. Vigorous exercise at
the end of the day can stimulate the mind and
body and make it harder to sleep at night.

WHERE DO YOU SLEEP?

The following elements help to enable good-quality sleep:

A cool (not cold), quiet and dark bedroom. Some people find it helpful to keep a window ajar during sleep, use earplugs and hang thick curtains (or wear an eye mask).

A good bed, with a suitable mattress and pillow. Consider the size of your bed, the firmness of your mattress and the feel of your pillow, and make sure that they all suit you. Select inviting bed linen, and have extra blankets ready for when it's cold.

Take a moment now and think about your bedroom. Is it comfortable, relaxing and somewhere that you want to sleep?

STEP TOWARDS REST

Step towards rest, a healthier sleeping pattern
and better-quality sleep with this simple guide.

Step one: Embrace your wakefulness and engage in a
relaxing activity before bed (e.g. reading, meditation or
colouring) in a calming environment with warm-coloured,
dim light. Choose a room that isn't your bedroom to
remind your mind that your bedroom is where you sleep.

Step two: Do not go to bed until you feel
tired and sleepy (even if it's getting late).

Step three: When you're in bed, turn off the lights.
See if you can welcome your feelings and acknowledge
your thoughts as best you can. Then, refocus your
attention and tune in to what you can touch and feel.
Be without judgement, and really experience simply
lying in bed! If your eyes do not close naturally, don't
force them shut. Let them be, and rest with your
eyes open. They'll close when they're ready to.

Step four: If you find yourself lying in bed for a long time and you're wide awake, then get up and repeat steps one to three. It may not feel like it now, but you will sleep again.

Step five: Set your alarm for the same time each day, e.g. 7 a.m., and get up when it sounds – even if you haven't had much sleep. Accept that you may feel tired, and commit to your new sleep schedule. Remind yourself why you've chosen to do this!

Step six: NO NAPS. Daytime naps can reduce the body's natural drive to sleep at night. See if you can observe the sleepy feelings come and go, and resist the urge to nap. Healthy distractions can help, such as going for a walk outside.

Try this new routine for several weeks, and see how you feel. You can reflect upon your experiences using the journal pages in this book.

'Be kind to yourself ...
You will come to see that
all evolves us.'

RUMI

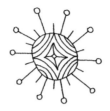

BRAINWAVES

Humans have different types of brainwaves that
correspond with how we're feeling and how we interact
with the environment around us. Beta brainwaves
are common in daily life when we're very alert,
problem-solving and decision-making. However, too
much time in 'beta' can leave us feeling stressed and
drained. Alpha brainwaves occur when we engage
with an activity that we find deeply relaxing. They are
associated with creativity, calmness and learning, and
help us to transition into sleep. You can encourage
your mind to wind down and produce more beneficial
alpha waves by doing something that you find
enriching and peaceful before bed, like colouring.

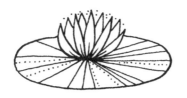

Many people have trouble sleeping at some point in their lives. I'm not alone in this.

WINDING DOWN

Transition into sleep slowly by giving yourself some time and space to wind down at the end of each day. Do something that's personally meaningful and calming for you before you go to bed, and only go to bed when you feel sleepy and tired. You could try reading, meditating or writing in this journal and colouring in. Choose something that absorbs your mind, rather than trying to bore yourself to sleep. 'Do something boring before bed' is a familiar sleep tip. However, this emphasis on the goal of sleep can actually push your readiness to sleep further away. Boredom can also encourage the mind to wander more than usual, which can be unhelpful.

SWITCH OFF

Research has found that the use of electronic screens (on TVs, laptops, tablets and smartphones) before bed can negatively affect our sleep and sleep patterns. They emit 'blue light' – a type of light (found naturally in the sun) that stimulates wakefulness, encourages the mind to be active, and suppresses the production of melatonin (a hormone which helps us to feel sleepy).

You may find it beneficial to turn off these devices at least one hour before you go to bed. Darkness and warm-coloured, dim light help to relax the mind, stimulate the production of melatonin and encourage restful sleep. Melatonin has antioxidant effects and health benefits too, so there's more than one reason to switch off at night!

'A ruffled mind makes
a restless pillow.'

CHARLOTTE BRONTË

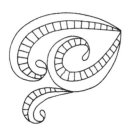

COMFORT AND CARE

Compassionate self-care is very important for good-quality sleep and emotional well-being. Consider how you treat yourself when you can't sleep. How do you respond to your sleeplessness?

The next time you can't sleep, try to do something nurturing for yourself, something soothing that will engage your senses and help to ground you in the present moment. You could try taking a warm bath with lavender oil, enjoying a chamomile tea or listening to some of your favourite music while colouring.

Ask yourself, *how can I comfort and care for myself right now?* Write your ideas down here, and try one of them tonight.

DESCRIBE THE THOUGHT

Can you spot the difference between
these two statements?

Statement one: *I won't be able to enjoy tomorrow.*
Vs.
Statement two: *I'm having a thought that
I won't be able to enjoy tomorrow.*

Statement one feels more intense, doesn't it? That's
because Statement two simply describes what the
mind is doing. It's having a thought! The thought itself
may not be 100% accurate or helpful. Describing your
thoughts can give you a little distance from them and
help to reduce their impact on you. It also enables
you to consider the thought, and then respond to it
in a helpful way. Why not try it yourself the next time
you notice a difficult thought, and see how you feel?

I'm having a thought that …
[describe the thought]

'A lion chased me up a tree,
and I greatly enjoyed the
view from the top.'

CONFUCIUS

WELCOMING ALL EMOTIONS

Allow yourself to really feel your emotions
tonight. 'Tune in' to yourself and use one word to
describe each emotion that you're experiencing
now (for example, frustrated, concerned
and hopeful). Write them down here.

Emotions are our messengers – they let us know
that something important is going on for us in a given
moment. See if you can welcome them all to be here
with you now, as best you can. You may not like what
you're experiencing, but it's a part of your reality in this
moment. You're allowed to feel this way! See if you
can notice your emotions without judgement
as they stay, change, come and go.

I can have a poor night's
sleep and still enjoy my
day tomorrow.

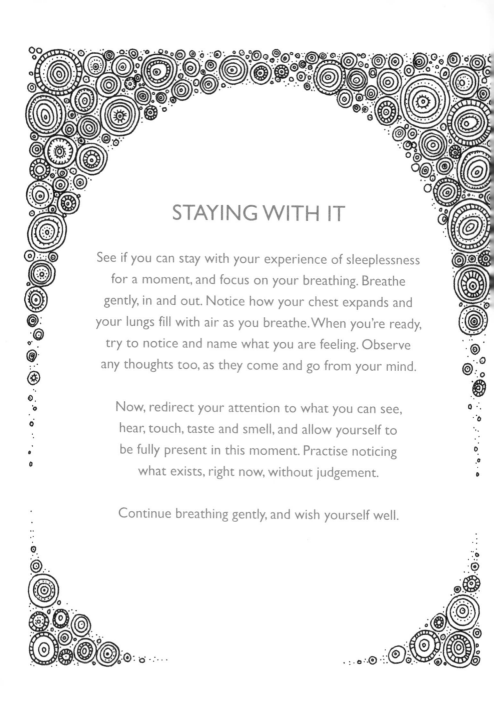

STAYING WITH IT

See if you can stay with your experience of sleeplessness
for a moment, and focus on your breathing. Breathe
gently, in and out. Notice how your chest expands and
your lungs fill with air as you breathe. When you're ready,
try to notice and name what you are feeling. Observe
any thoughts too, as they come and go from your mind.

Now, redirect your attention to what you can see,
hear, touch, taste and smell, and allow yourself to
be fully present in this moment. Practise noticing
what exists, right now, without judgement.

Continue breathing gently, and wish yourself well.

'Everything flows and nothing
abides; everything gives way
and nothing stays fixed.'

HERACLITUS

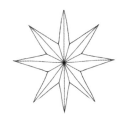

SAY 'NO' TO CLOCK-WATCHING

Checking the time when you're in bed can wake up
the mind, reinforce unhelpful thoughts and create
stress. Combat this by removing unnecessary clocks
from the bedroom and keep your alarm clock or
phone out of sight at night. Notice if you get the urge
to check the time. Remind yourself that this urge
is understandable but unhelpful, and choose not to
check the time in favour of your own well-being.

'When you arise in the morning,
think of what a precious privilege
it is to be alive – to breathe,
to think, to enjoy, to love.'

MARCUS AURELIUS

WHAT'S ON YOUR MIND?

This time is yours. Write about whatever is
on your mind tonight. Hopes, fears, troubles,
dreams … All are welcome here.

I may feel very tired
tomorrow, but I will still
be able to function.

GRATITUDE

Practising gratitude can have a positive effect on sleep, physical health and psychological well-being. It enables recognition of what we have in the present moment, and it supports positive coping with stressful situations.

Every day, in a moment that suits you, name three things for which you feel genuinely grateful and write them down. Try this practice every day for the next two weeks and notice how you feel.

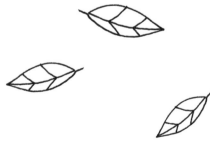

FURTHER RESOURCES FOR
WELL-BEING AND GOOD SLEEP

Books

Arnold, S. J. *The Mindfulness Companion*. Michael O'Mara Books, 2016.

Branch, R. *Cognitive Behavioural Therapy for Dummies*. John Wiley & Sons, 2010.

Collard, P. *The Mindfulness Bible: The Complete Guide to Living in the Moment*. Godsfield Press, 2015.

Espie, C. *Overcoming Insomnia and Sleep Problems: A Self-Help Guide Using Cognitive Behavioral Techniques*. Robinson, 2006.

Meadows, G. *The Sleep Book: How to Sleep Well Every Night*. Orion, 2014.

Websites

For more information about sleep and support with sleep problems:

www.howsleepworks.com/hygiene.html
www.thesleepschool.org
www.sleepfoundation.org

Emotional difficulties and life stresses can manifest as sleep problems. Here are some brilliant, free resources on various topics (including worry, depression and assertiveness). They can help you to sleep better too:

www.cci.health.wa.gov.au/resources/consumers.cfm

Self-compassion is associated with well-being and good-quality sleep. You may find the following exercises helpful:

www.self-compassion.org/category/exercises/#exercises

Research tells us that mindfulness meditation can reduce stress and help to improve sleep. For more about what mindfulness is, and how to do it, check out these great sites:

www.themindfulnesssummit.com
www.franticworld.com/resources
www.headspace.com/sleep-meditation

A WORD OF CAUTION

If you are experiencing insomnia or another sleep disorder (like night terrors, sleep-walking, narcolepsy or hypersomnia), and are finding it hard to cope, you may benefit from talking to a mental health professional who specializes in helping people with sleep problems. Seek advice from your doctor or local counselling service to find out about your options.

ABOUT THE AUTHOR

Dr Sarah Jane Arnold is a Chartered Counselling
Psychologist. In her private practice she works with
people experiencing life issues, including sleep problems,
as well as specific mental health difficulties like anxiety
and depression. Using mindfulness-informed, integrative
psychological therapy, Sarah supports individuals to
understand their difficulties and break free from limiting
vicious cycles so that they can live
a full and meaningful life.

Sarah lives in Brighton, in the UK, with her partner, Mine,
their dog, Oprah, and Priscilla the bearded dragon.
You can find her online at
www.themindfulpsychologist.co.uk.